# WEDDING SHEET MUSIC HITS

**Arranged by DAN COATES**

Published 2004

© International Music Publications Ltd
Griffin House 161 Hammersmith Road London W6 8BS England

Editorial management: Artemis Music Limited (www.artemismusic.com)

8.95

# All I Have

Words and Music by Beth Nielsen Chapman and Eric Kaz

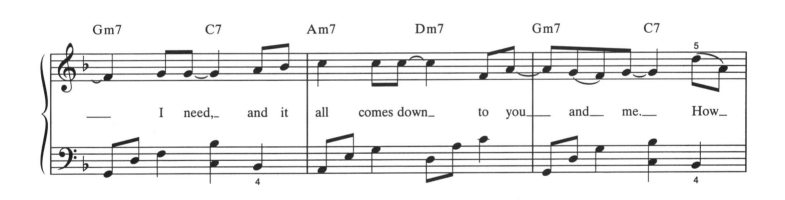
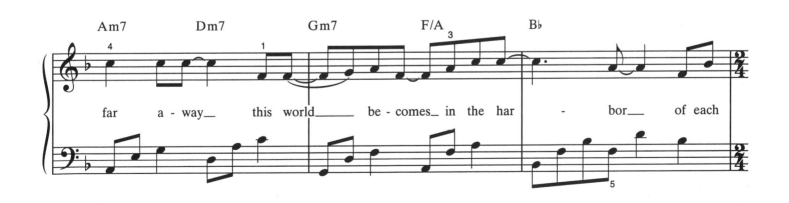

4

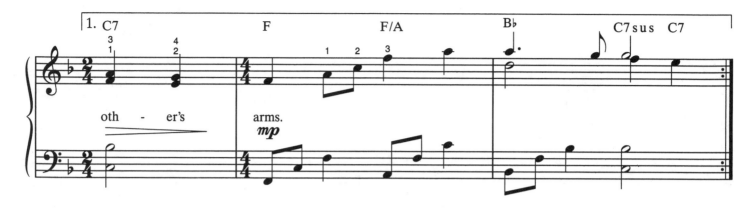

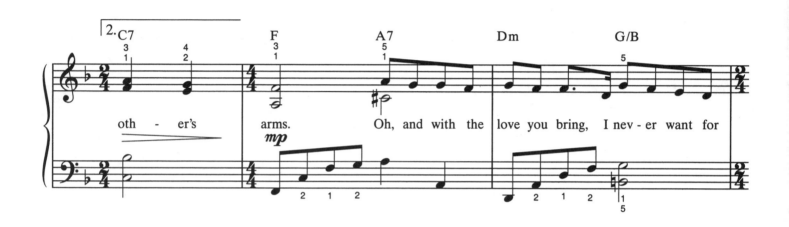

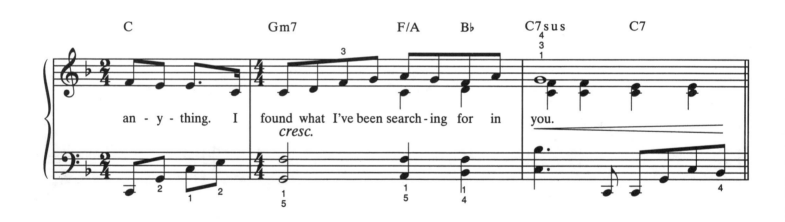

*Chorus:*

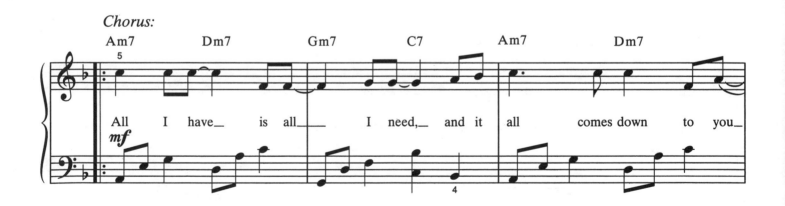

*Verse 2:*
I feel like I've known you
Forever and ever, baby,
That's how close we are.
Right here with you is where my life
Has come together,
And where love has filled my heart.
You know I'd go anywhere
As long as I have you to care.
*(To Chorus:)*

# Always

Written by Jonathan Lewis, Wayne Lewis and David Lewis

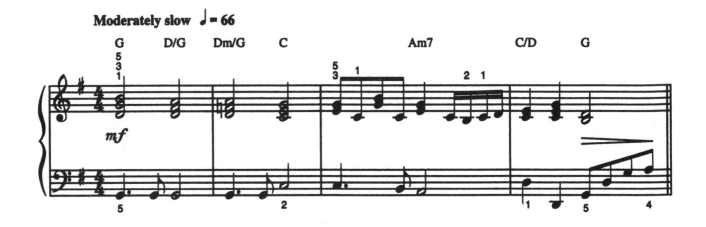

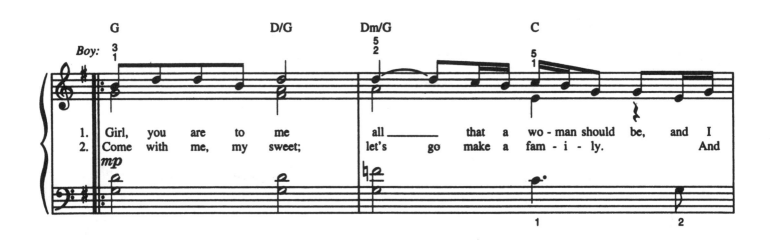

1. Girl, you are to me all ____ that a wo-man should be, and I
2. Come with me, my sweet; let's go make a fam-i-ly. And

ded-i-cate my life to you al - ways. A love like yours is rare; it
they will bring us joy for al - ways. Oh, boy, I love you so; I can't

7

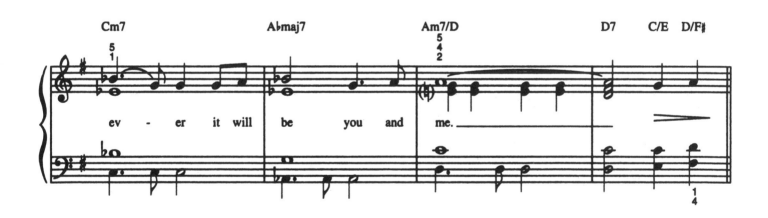

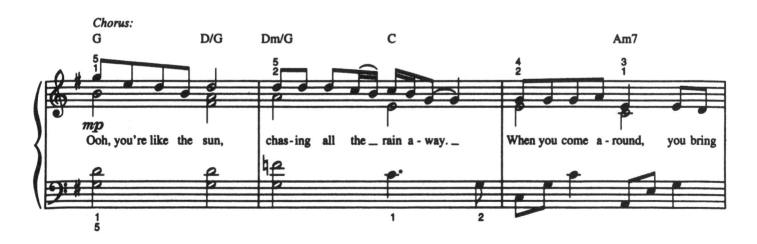

8

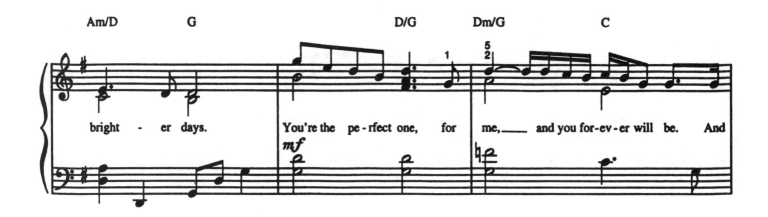

bright - er days. You're the pe - rfect one, for me,___ and you for-ev-er will be. And

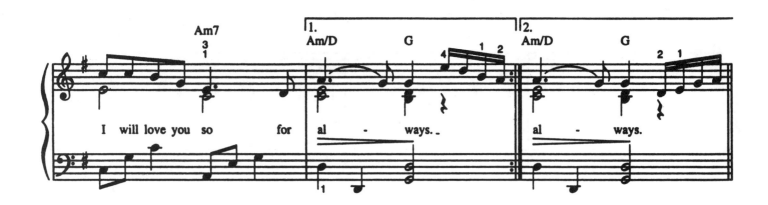

I will love you so for al - ways.. al - ways.

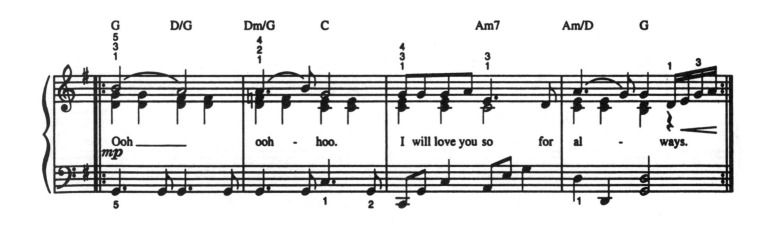

Ooh ___ ooh - hoo. I will love you so for al - ways.

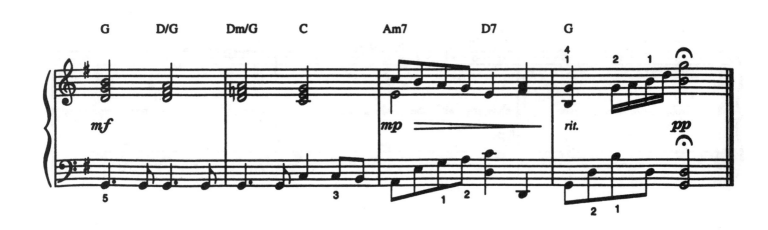

# Amazed

Words and Music by Marv Green, Aimee Mayo and Chris Lindsey

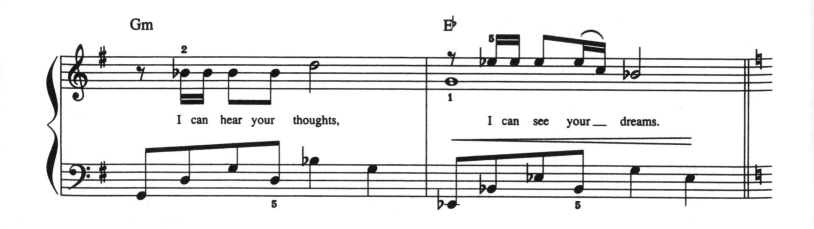

I can hear your thoughts,

I can see your ___ dreams.

*Chorus:*

I don't know how you do what you do. ___

I'm so in love with

you.

It just keeps get - ting bet - ter.

I wan - na spend the rest of my life ___

with you by my side ___

12

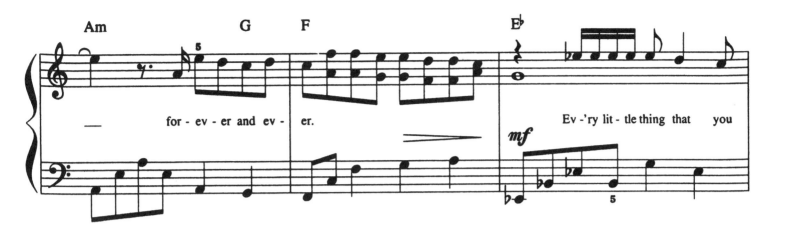

for - ev - er and ev - er.                 Ev -'ry lit - tle thing that    you

do,    (ev -'ry lit - tle thing that    you    do...)    ev -'ry lit - tle thing that    you_____

do,    ba - by, I'm a - mazed    by_____    you.

*Verse 2:*
The smell of your skin,
The taste of your kiss,
The way you whisper in the dark.
Your hair all around me,
Baby, you surround me.
You touch every place in my heart.
Oh, it feels like the first time every time.
I wanna spend the whole night in your eyes.
*(To Chorus:)*

# At Last

Words by Mack Gordon
Music by Harry Warren

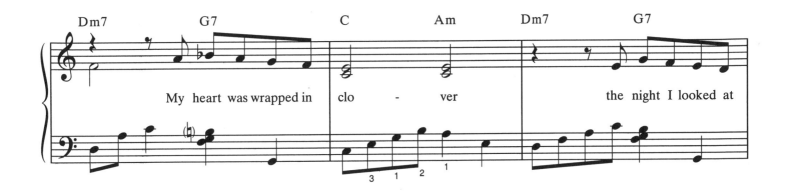

My heart was wrapped in clo - ver the night I looked at

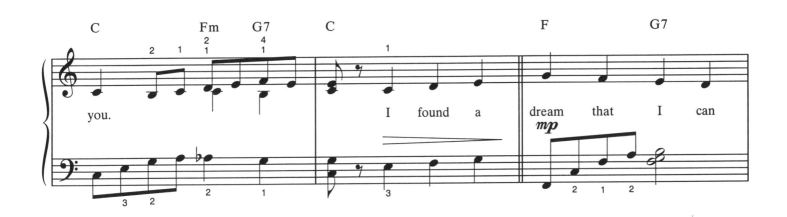

you. I found a dream that I can

speak to, a dream that I can call my own. I found a

thrill to press my cheek to, a thrill I've nev - er

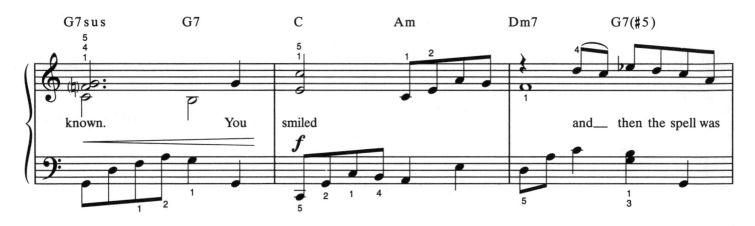

known.         You  smiled                      and__ then the spell was

cast.                     And__ here we are in heav - en

for you are mine__ at__ last.                   At

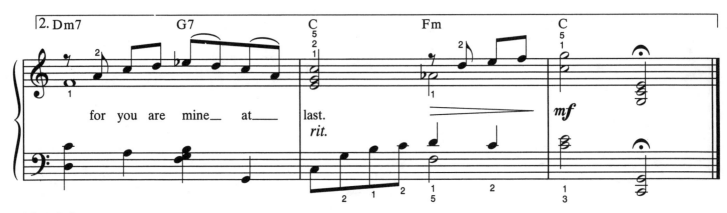

for you are mine__ at__ last.                   

*rit.*

At Last - 3 - 3

# Endless Love

Words and Music by Lionel Richie

Endless Love - 5 - 5

# Ave Maria

Words by Sir Walter Scott
Music by Franz Schubert

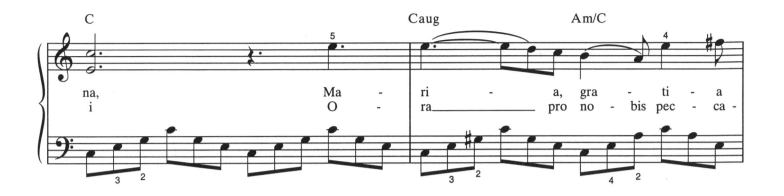

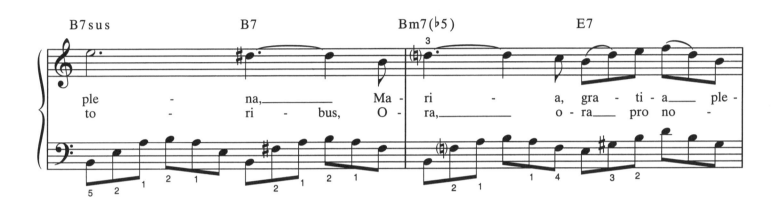

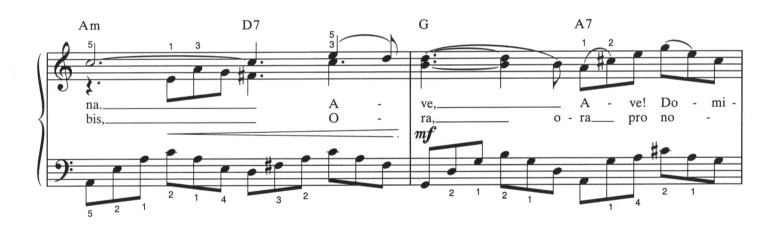

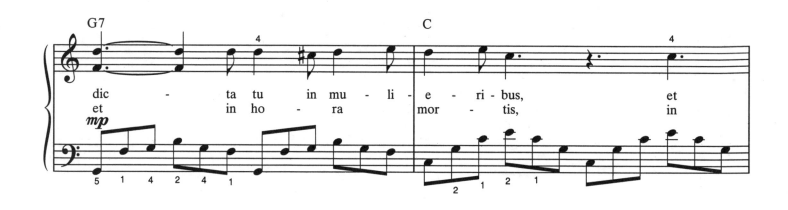

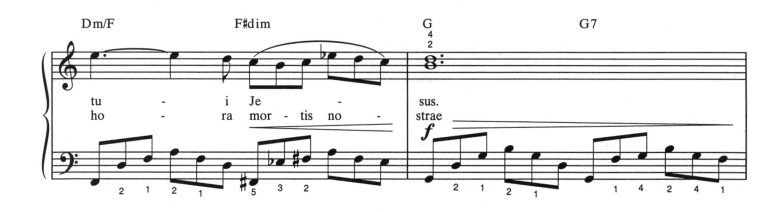

# Bridal Chorus

Music by Richard Wagner

D.S. al Fine

# Can You Feel The Love Tonight

Words by Tim Rice
Music by Elton John

# How Deep Is Your Love

Words and Music by Barry Gibb, Robin Gibb and Maurice Gibb

Warner/Chappell Music Ltd, London W6 8BS and BMG Music Publishing Ltd, London  SW6 3JW

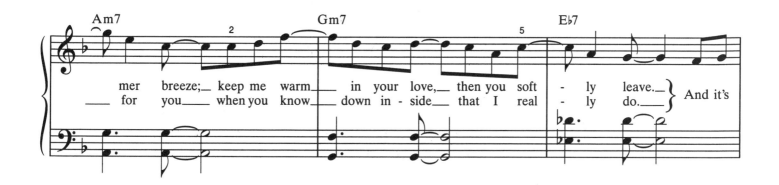

mer breeze;__ keep me warm__ in your love,__ then you soft - ly leave.__ And it's
for you__ when you know__ down in - side__ that I real - ly do.__

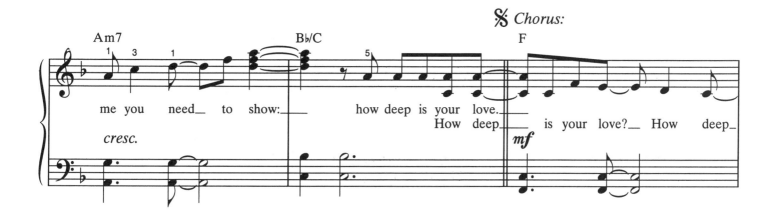

𝄋 *Chorus:*

me you need__ to show:__ how deep is your love.__
How deep__ is your love?__ How deep_

*cresc.*    *mf*

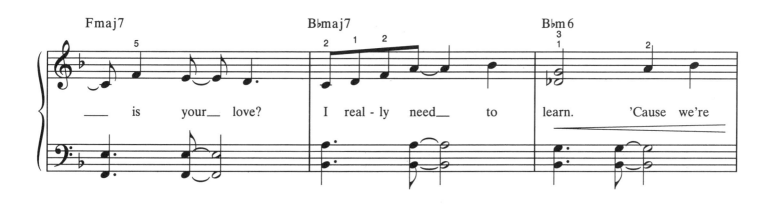

__ is your__ love? I real - ly need__ to learn. 'Cause we're

liv - ing in a world of fools,__ break - ing us down when they all__

*f*

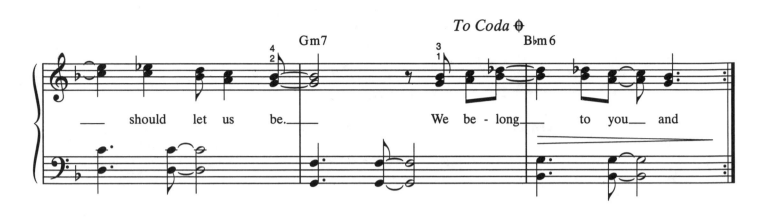

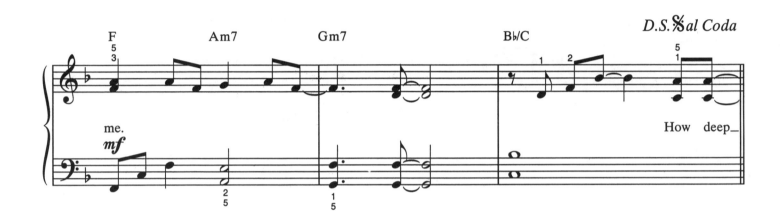

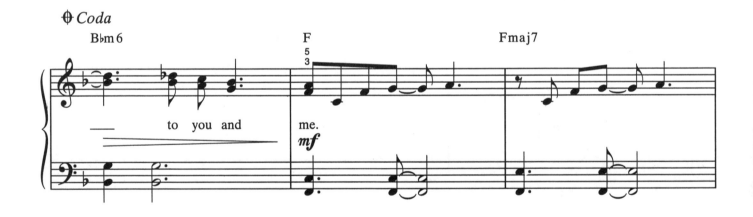

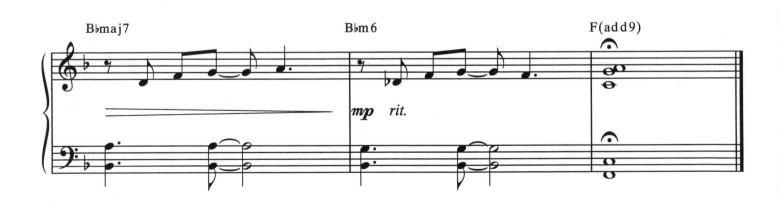

# I Just Called To Say I Love You

Words and Music by Stevie Wonder

*Verse 3:*
No summer's high; no warm July;
No harvest moon to light one tender August night.
No autumn breeze; no falling leaves;
Not even time for birds to fly to southern skies.

*Verse 4:*
No Libra sun; no Halloween;
No giving thanks to all the Christmas joy you bring.
But what it is, though old so new
To fill your heart like no three words could ever do.
*(To Chorus:)*

# I Get A Kick Out Of You
## (from *Anything Goes*)

Words and Music by Cole Porter

**Moderately, with motion**

I get no kick from cham - pagne,

mere al - co - hol does - n't thrill me at all. So

tell me why should it be true,_____ that

# I Swear

Words and Music by Gary Baker and Frank Myers

43

# I Will Always Love You

Words and Music by Dolly Parton

*Extra Lyrics:*

3. I hope life treats you kind
   And I hope you have all you've dreamed of.
   I wish you joy and happiness.
   But above all this,
   I wish you love.

# Love Like Ours

Words by Alan Bergman and Marilyn Bergman
Music by Dave Grusin

lone - ly, to find the one and on - ly.

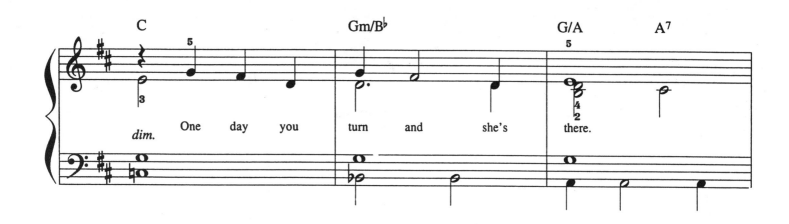

One day you turn and she's there.

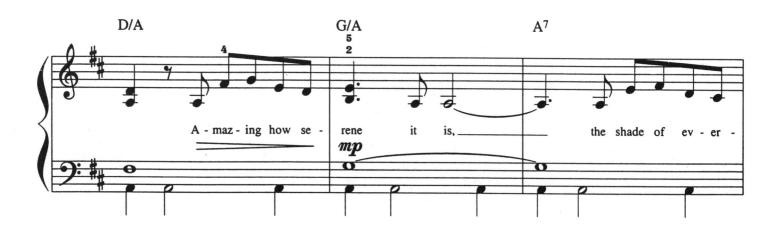

A - maz - ing how se - rene it is, the shade of ev - er -

green it is, ex - act - ly what we mean it is, and

# In Your Eyes

Words and Music by Michael Masser and Daniel Hill

*Verse 2:*
But you warned me that life changes,
And that no one really knows
Whether time would make us grow.
Even though the winds of time will change
In a world where nothing stays the same,
Through it all our love will still remain.
*(To Chorus:)*

# I've Got You Under My Skin

Words and Music by Cole Porter

58

# My Heart Will Go On

Words by Will Jennings
Music by James Horner

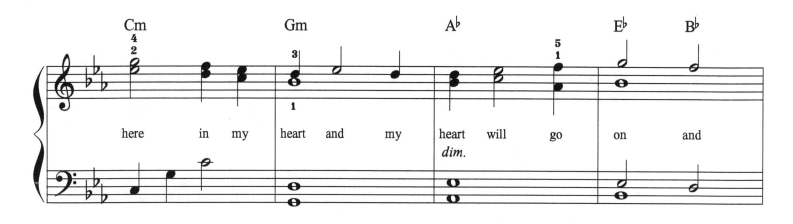

here   in   my   heart   and   my   heart   will   go   on   and
*dim.*

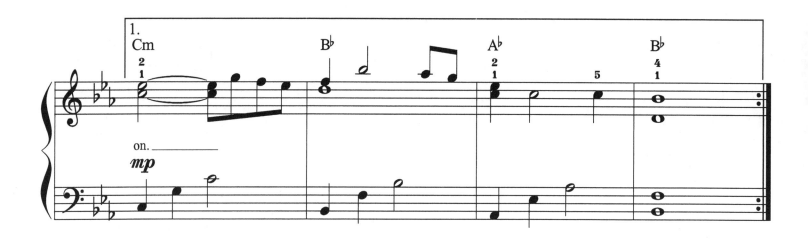

on. _____
*mp*

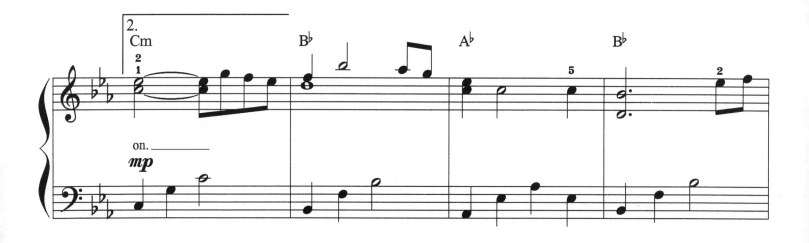

on. _____
*mp*

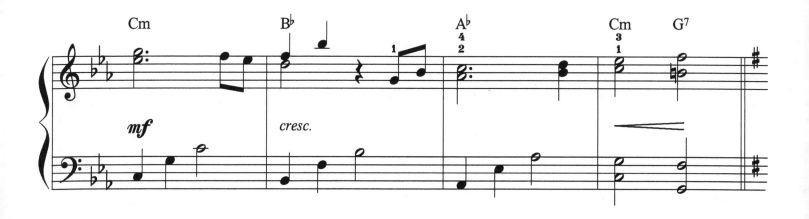

*mf*      *cresc.*

# Once In A Lifetime

Words and Music by Michael Bolton, Walter Afanasieff and Diane Warren

66

# The Power Of Love

Words by Jennifer Rush and Mary Applegate
Music by Candy De Rouge and Gunthe Mende

*Verse 2:*
Lost is how I'm feeling
Lying in your arms.
When the world outside's too much to take
That all end's when I'm with you.
Even though there may be times
It seems I'm far away,
Never wonder where I am
'Cause I am always by your side.
*(To Chorus:)*

# Tonight I Celebrate My Love

Words and Music by Michael Masser and Gerry Goffin

**Slowly**

*Verse 3:*

Tonight I celebrate my love for you
And soon this old world will seem brand new.
Tonight we will both discover
How friends turn into lovers.
When I make love to you.

# This Magic Moment

Words and Music by Doc Pomus and Mort Shuman

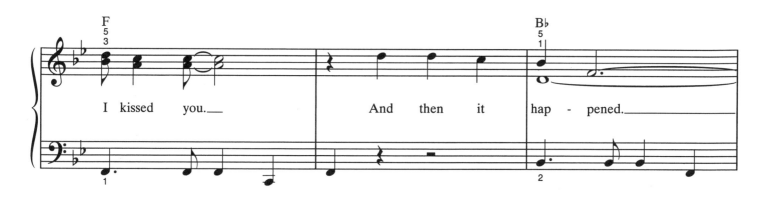

I kissed you.＿ And then it hap - pened.＿

＿ It took me by＿ sur - prise.＿ I knew that you

felt it, too＿ by the look in your eyes,＿

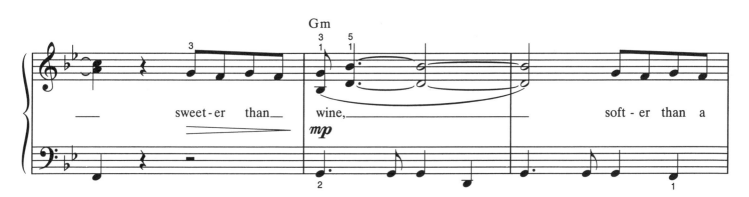

＿ sweet - er than＿ wine, soft - er than a

sum-mer night._____ Ev-'ry-thing I want I have_____
*cresc.*

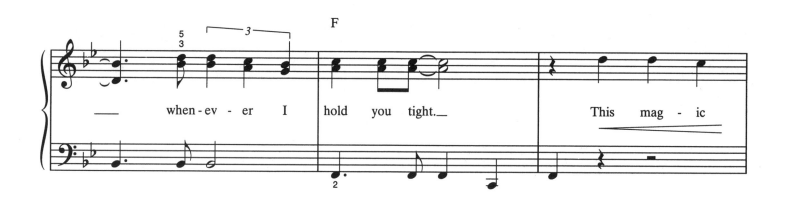

_____ when-ev-er I hold you tight.____ This mag-ic

mo - ment,_____ while your lips are close__ to mine,__

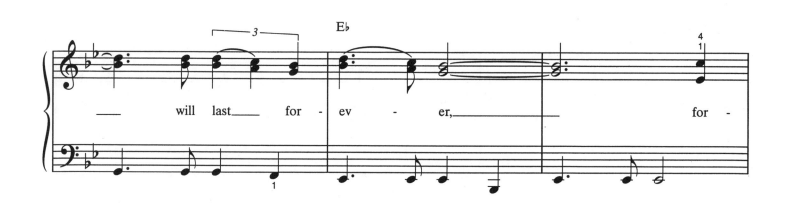

____ will last____ for - ev - er,_____ for -

# The Wedding March

Music by Felix Mendelssohn

# The Wedding Song
## (There Is Love)

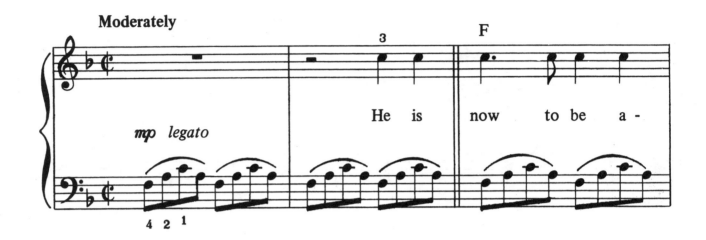

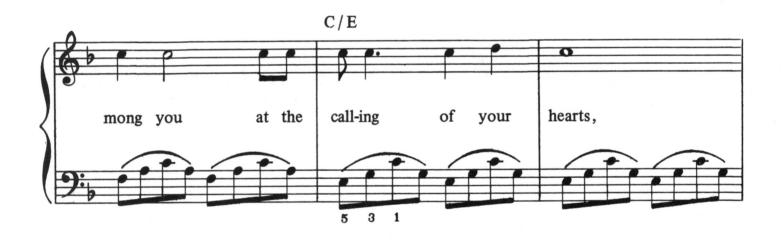

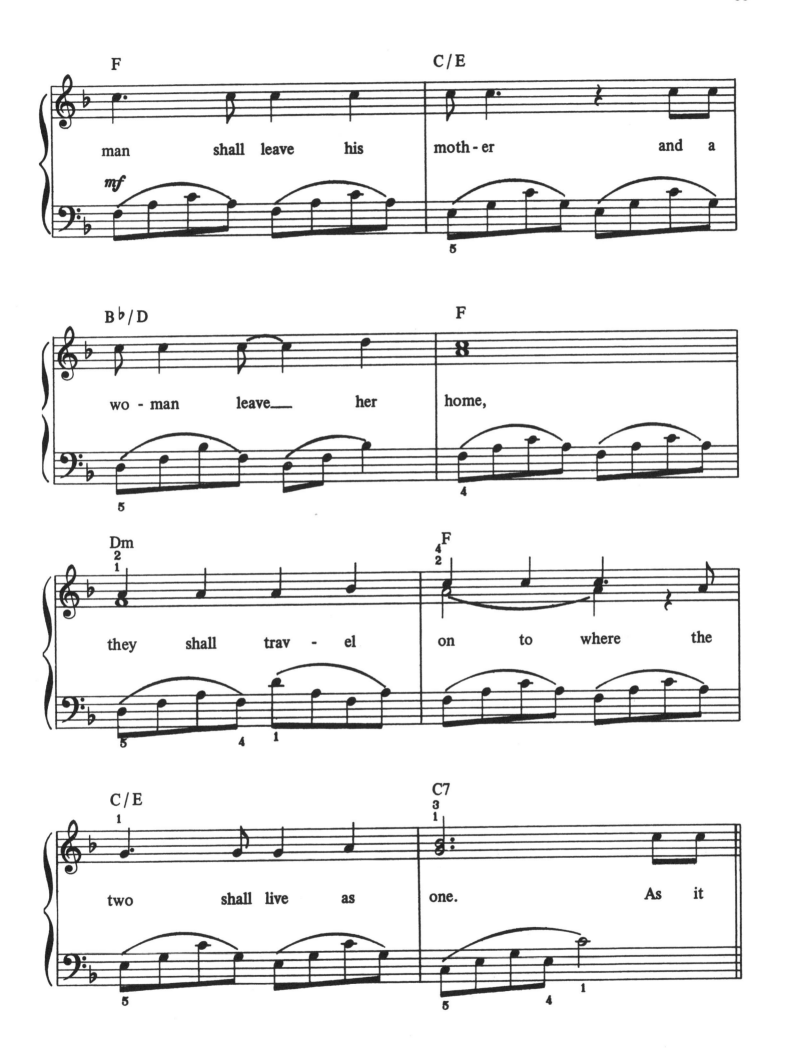

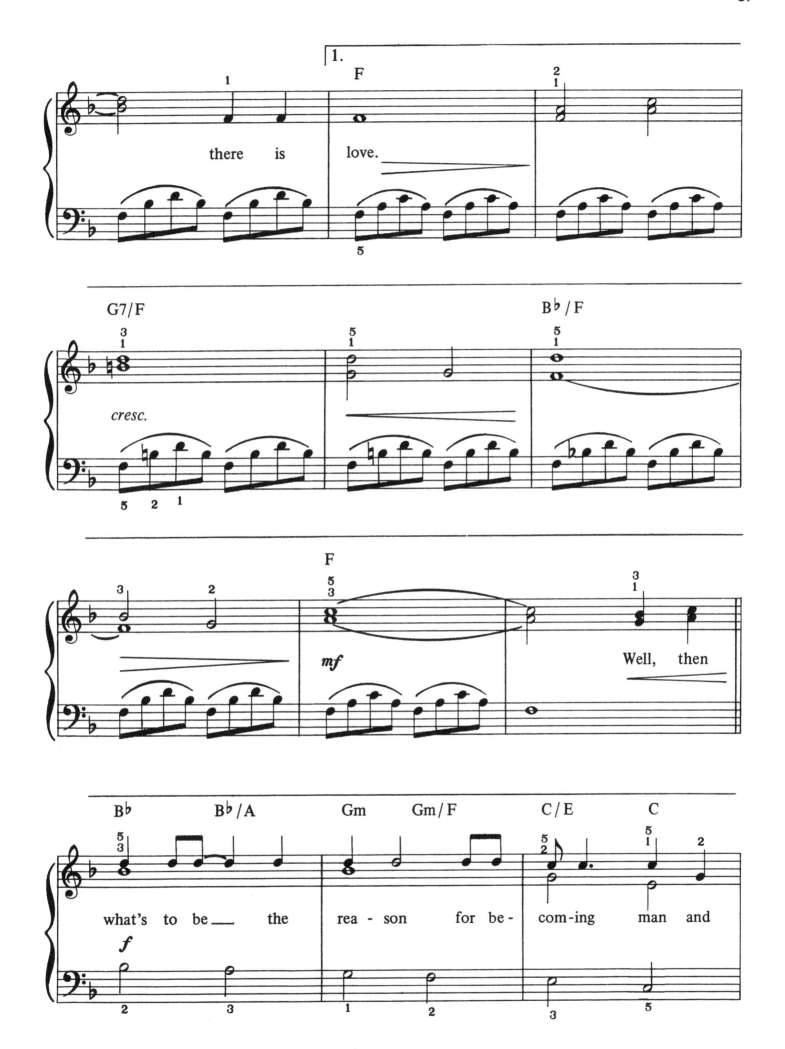

# With This Ring (I Thee Wed)

Words by Remus Harris
Music by John Sacco

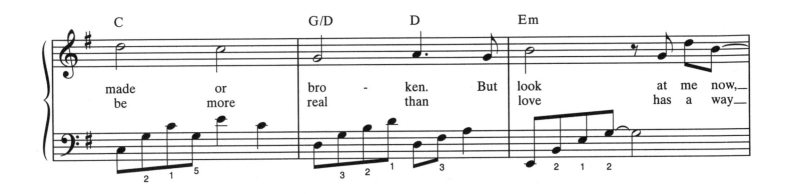

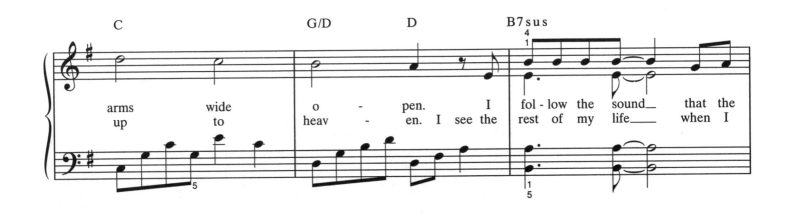

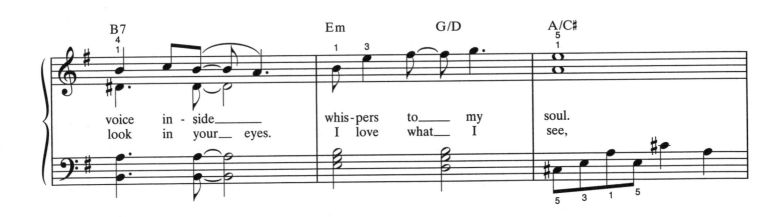

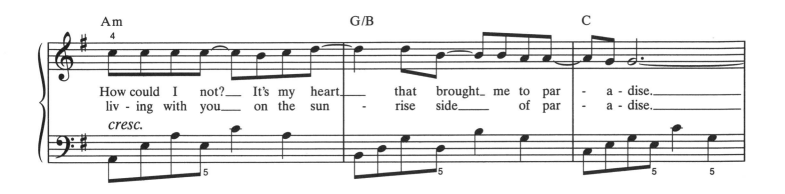

How could I not?__ It's my heart__ that brought_ me to par - a - dise.___
liv - ing with you__ on the sun - rise side_____ of par - a - dise.___

cresc.

%S *Chorus:*

I'll be your lov - er, I'll be your friend.__ I'll be the sum-

mf

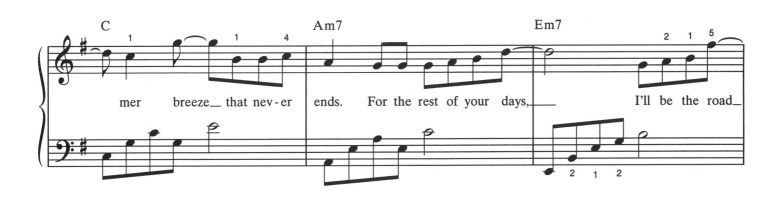

mer breeze__ that nev - er ends. For the rest of your days,__ I'll be the road_

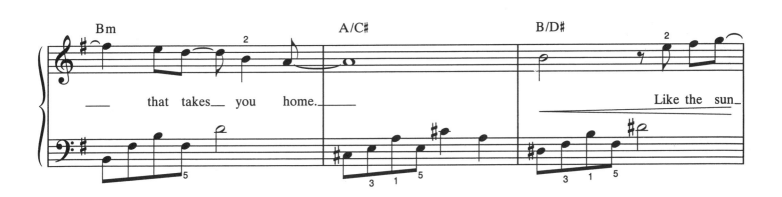

__ that takes__ you home.__ Like the sun_

92

# You're The Inspiration

Words and Music by Peter Cetera and David Foster

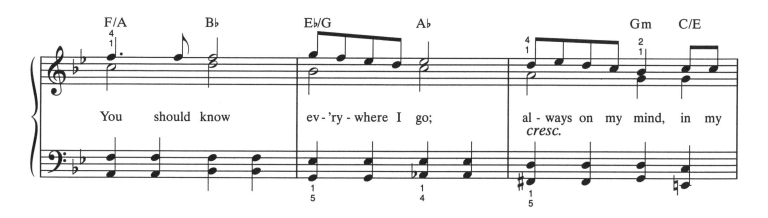

You should know ev-'ry-where I go; al - ways on my mind, in my

*cresc.*

*Chorus:*

heart, in my soul, ba - by. You're the mean-ing of my life, you're the in-spi-ra-tion.

*mf*

You bring feel-ing to my life, you're the in-spi-ra-tion. Wan-na have you near me, I

*f*

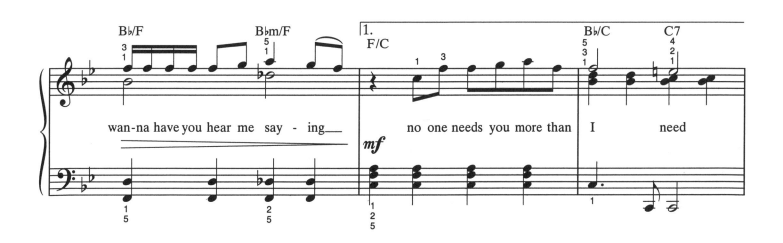

wan-na have you hear me say - ing___ no one needs you more than I need

*mf*

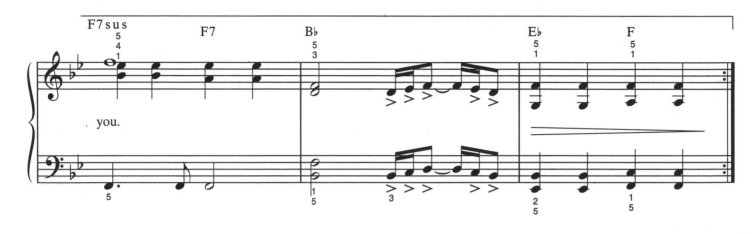

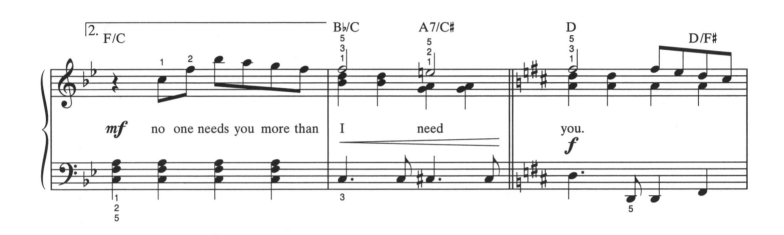

no one needs you more than I need you.

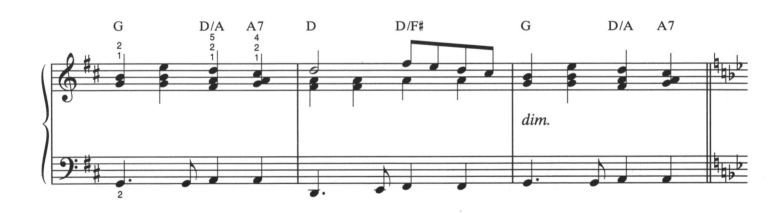

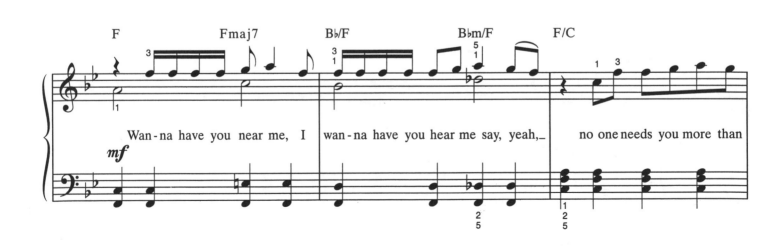

Wan-na have you near me, I wan-na have you hear me say, yeah,_ no one needs you more than

*Verse 2:*
And I know (yes, I know)
That it's plain to see
We're so in love when we're together.
Now I know (now I know)
That I need you here with me
From tonight until the end of time.
You should know everywhere I go;
Always on my mind, you're in my heart, in my soul.
*(To Chorus:)*

# Your Love Amazes Me

Words and Music by Chuck Jones and Amanda Hunt

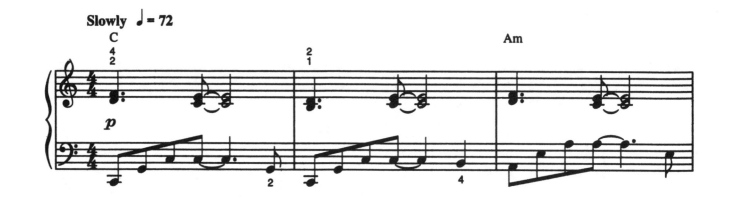

1. I've seen the sev-en won-ders

of the world._ I've seen the beau-ty of dia-monds and pearls._

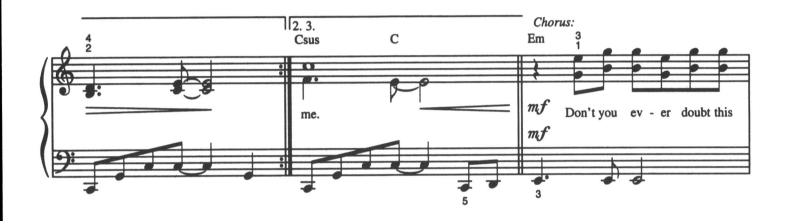

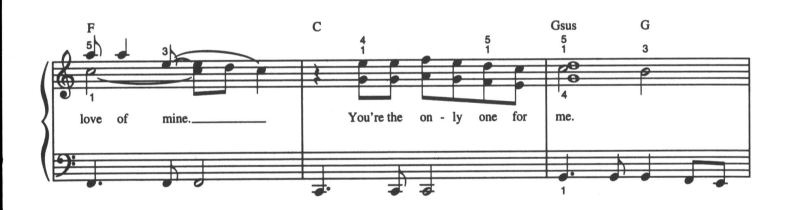

For - ev - er faith - ful - ly, your love a - maz - es me.

Your love, your love,___

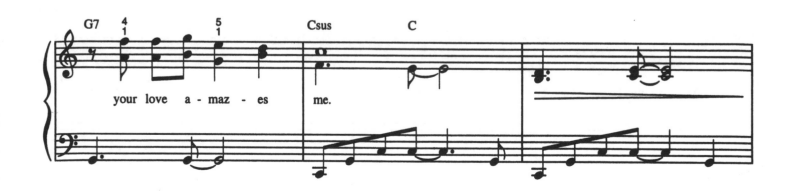

your love a - maz - es me.

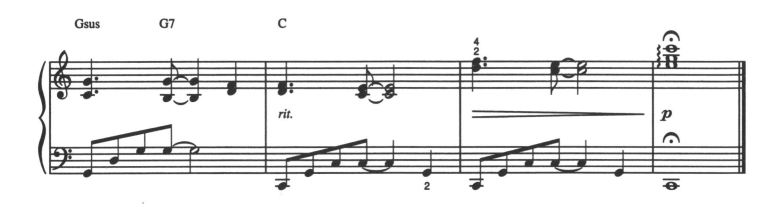

*Verse 2:*
I've seen a sunset that would make you cry,
And colors of a rainbow reaching 'cross the sky.
The moon in all its phases, but
Your love amazes me.
*(To Chorus:)*

*Verse 3:*
I've prayed for miracles that never came.
I got down on my knees in the pouring rain.
But only you could save me,
Your love amazes me.
*(To Chorus:)*

# The Easy Piano Library

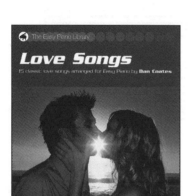
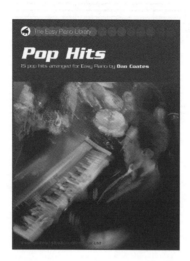

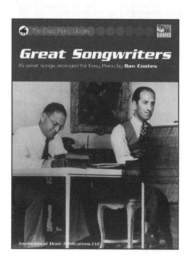

## LOVE SONGS
*9544A          E/PNO          ISBN: 1-84328-115-5*

Angel Of Mine - Because You Loved Me - Get Here - The Greatest Love Of All - Have I Told You Lately That I Love You - I'd Lie For You (And That's The Truth) - I Turn To You - Now And Forever - The Prayer - Right Here Waiting - The Rose - Something About The Way You Look Tonight - Unbreak My Heart - When You Tell Me That You Love Me - 2 Become 1

## POP HITS
*9546A          E/PNO          ISBN: 1-84328-117-1*

Amazed - Believe - Can't Fight The Moonlight - Genie In A Bottle - Heal The World - How Do I Live - I'll Be There For You - Kiss The Rain - Livin' La Vida Loca - Macarena - Music - Quit Playing Games With My Heart - Smooth - Swear It Again - Thank You

## FILM FAVOURITES
*9545A          E/PNO          ISBN: 1-84328-116-3*

Batman Theme - Beautiful Stranger - Because You Loved Me - Can You Feel The Love Tonight - Can't Fight The Moonlight - Evergreen - (Everything I Do) I Do It For You - I Don't Want To Miss A Thing - Imperial March (Darth Vader's Theme) - I Will Always Love You - Somewhere My Love (Lara's Theme) - Star Wars (Main Theme) - Superman Theme - Wind Beneath My Wings

## ALL TIME GREATS
*9603A          E/PNO          ISBN: 1-84328-138-4*

American Pie – As Time Goes By – Desperado – The Greatest Love Of All – Hotel California – Lean On Me – My Heart Will Go On – My Way – Over The Rainbow – Sacrifice – Save The Best For Last – Send In The Clowns – Stairway To Heaven – Theme From New York, New York – When You Tell Me That You Love Me

## GREAT SONGWRITERS
*9671A          E/PNO          ISBN: 1-84328-175-3*

As Time Goes By – Bewitched – Cabaret – High Hopes – I Got Plenty O' Nuttin' – It Ain't Necessarily So – Love & Marriage – Maybe This Time – Never Met A Man I Din't Like – Over The Rainbow – Raindrops Keep Fallin' On My Head – Send In The Clowns – Singin' In The Rain – Summertime – Tomorrow

## CHRISTMAS SONGS
*9790A          E/PNO          ISBN: 1-84328-309-3*

All I Want For Christmas Is My Two Front Teeth - Deck The Hall - It's The Most Wonderful Time Of The Year - Jingle Bells - Let it Snow! Let it Snow! Let it Snow! - The Little Drummer Boy - Little Saint Nick - Have Yourself A Merry Little Christmas - I Believe In Santa Claus - The Most Wonderful Day Of The Year - O Christmas Tree - Rockin' Around The Christmas Tree - Rudolph, The Red-Nosed Reindeer - Santa Claus Is Comin' To Town - Sleigh Ride - The Twelve Days Of Christmas - Winter Wonderland

# An expansive series of over 50 titles!

Each song features melody line, vocals, chord displays, suggested registrations and rhythm settings.

"For each title ALL the chords (both 3 finger and 4 finger) used are shown in the correct position - which makes a change!" **Organ & Keyboard Cavalcade, May 2001**

Each song appears on two facing pages eliminating the need to turn the page during performance. We have just introduced a new cover look to the series and will repackage the backlist in the same way.

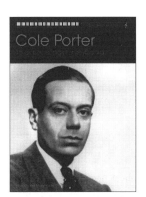

# YOU'RE THE VOICE

**8861A PV/CD**
Casta Diva from Norma – Vissi D'arte from Tosca – Un Bel Di Vedremo from Madama Butterfly – Addio, Del Passato from La Traviata – J'ai Perdu Mon Eurydice from Orphee Et Eurydice – Les Tringles Des Sistres Tintaient from Carmen – Porgi Amor from Le Nozze Di Figaro – Ave Maria from Otello

**8860A PVG/CD**
Delilah – Green Green Grass Of Home – Help Yourself – I'll Never Fall In Love Again – It's Not Unusual – Mama Told Me Not To Come – Sexbomb – Thunderball – What's New Pussycat – You Can Leave Your Hat On

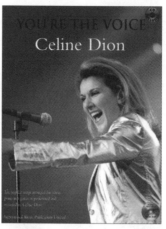

**9297A PVG/CD**
Beauty And The Beast – Because You Loved Me – Falling Into You – The First Time Ever I Saw Your Face – It's All Coming Back To Me Now – Misled – My Heart Will Go On – The Power Of Love – Think Twice – When I Fall In Love

**9349A PVG/CD**
Chain Of Fools – A Deeper Love Do Right Woman, Do Right Man – I Knew You Were Waiting (For Me) – I Never Loved A Man (The Way I Loved You) – I Say A Little Prayer – Respect – Think – Who's Zooming Who – (You Make Me Feel Like) A Natural Woman

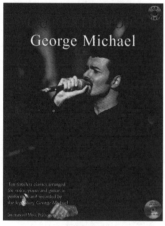

**9007A PVG/CD**
Careless Whisper – A Different Corner – Faith – Father Figure – Freedom '90 – I'm Your Man – I Knew You Were Waiting (For Me) – Jesus To A Child – Older – Outside

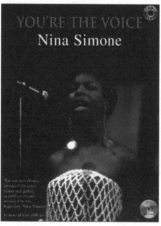

**9606A PVG/CD**
Don't Let Me Be Misunderstood – Feeling Good – I Loves You Porgy – I Put A Spell On You – Love Me Or Leave Me – Mood Indigo – My Baby Just Cares For Me – Ne Me Quitte Pas (If You Go Away) – Nobody Knows You When You're Down And Out – Take Me To The Water

**9700A PVG/CD**
Beautiful – Crying In The Rain – I Feel The Earth Move – It's Too Late – (You Make Me Feel Like) A Natural Woman – So Far Away – Way Over Yonder – Where You Lead – Will You Love Me Tomorrow – You've Got A Friend

**9746A PVG/CD**
April In Paris – Come Rain Or Come Shine – Fly Me To The Moon (In Other Words) – I've Got You Under My Skin – The Lady Is A Tramp – My Kinda Town (Chicago Is) – My Way – Theme From *New York, New York* – Someone To Watch Over Me – Something Stupid

**9770A PVG/CD**
Cry Me A River – Evergreen (A Star Is Born) – Happy Days Are Here Again – I've Dreamed Of You – Memory – My Heart Belongs To Me – On A Clear Day (You Can See Forever) – Someday My Prince Will Come – Tell Him (duet with Celine Dion) – The Way We Were

**9799A PVG/CD**
Boogie Woogie Bugle Boy – Chapel Of Love – Friends – From A Distance – Hello In There – One For My Baby (And One More For The Road) – Only In Miami – The Rose – When A Man Loves A Woman – Wind Beneath My Wings

**9810A PVG/CD**
Ain't No Sunshine – Autumn Leaves – How Can I Keep From Singing – Imagine – It Doesn't Matter Anymore – Over The Rainbow – Penny To My Name – People Get Ready – Wayfaring Stranger – What A Wonderful World

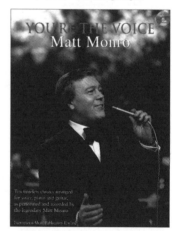

**9889A PVG/CD**
Around The World – Born Free – From Russia With Love – Gonna Build A Mountain – The Impossible Dream – My Kind Of Girl – On A Clear Day You Can See Forever – Portrait Of My Love – Softly As I Leave You – Walk Away

## The outstanding vocal series from IMP

### CD contains full backings for each song, professionally arranged to recreate the sounds of the original recording